# BATGIRL

## Destruction's Daughter

 ## Destruction's Daughter

Andersen Gabrych
**Writer**

Pop Mhan
Alé Garza
Francisco Rodriguez de la Fuente
Andy Kuhn
**Pencillers**

Jesse Delperdang
Cam Smith
Andy Kuhn
Dan Davis
Adam DeKraker
Rodney Ramos
Robin Riggs
**Inkers**

Jason Wright
WildStorm FX
Guy Major
**Colorists**

Pat Brosseau
Jared K. Fletcher
Nick J. Napolitano
Rob Leigh
**Letterers**

Batman created by Bob Kane

Dan DiDio
Senior VP-Executive Editor

Michael Wright
Editor-original series

Anton Kawasaki
Editor-collected edition

Robbin Brosterman
Senior Art Director

Paul Levitz
President & Publisher

Georg Brewer
VP-Design & DC Direct Creative

Richard Bruning
Senior VP-Creative Director

Patrick Caldon
Executive VP-Finance & Operations

Chris Caramalis
VP-Finance

John Cunningham
VP-Marketing

Terri Cunningham
VP-Managing Editor

Stephanie Fierman
Senior VP-Sales & Marketing

Alison Gill
VP-Manufacturing

Hank Kanalz
VP-General Manager, WildStorm

Lillian Laserson
Senior VP & General Counsel

Jim Lee
Editorial Director-WildStorm

Paula Lowitt
Senior VP-Business & Legal Affairs

David McKillips
VP-Advertising & Custom Publishing

John Nee
VP-Business Development

Gregory Noveck
Senior VP-Creative Affairs

Cheryl Rubin
Senior VP-Brand Management

Jeff Trojan
VP-Business Development, DC Direct

Bob Wayne
VP-Sales

# Batgirl: Destruction's Daughter

Published by DC Comics. Cover and compilation copyright © 2006
DC Comics. All Rights Reserved.

Originally published in single magazine form in BATGIRL #65-73.
Copyright © 2005, 2006 DC Comics. All Rights Reserved. All characters, their distinctive likenesses and related elements featured in
this publication are trademarks of DC Comics. The stories, characters
and incidents featured in this publication are entirely fictional.
DC Comics does not read or accept unsolicited submissions of ideas,
stories or artwork.

DC Comics, 1700 Broadway, New York, NY 10019
A Warner Bros. Entertainment Company
Printed in Canada. First Printing.
ISBN: 1-4012-0896-7
ISBN 13: 978-1-4012-0896-7
Cover by Tim Sale.

"A Mother of a Father's Day"
Pop Mhan – Pencils  Cam Smith – Inks

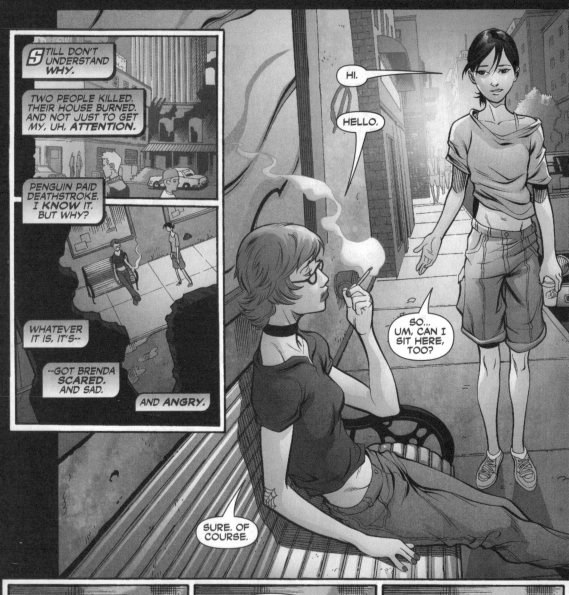

STILL DON'T UNDERSTAND WHY.

TWO PEOPLE KILLED. THEIR HOUSE BURNED. AND NOT JUST TO GET MY, UH, ATTENTION.

PENGUIN PAID DEATHSTROKE. I KNOW IT. BUT WHY?

WHATEVER IT IS, IT'S--

--GOT BRENDA SCARED. AND SAD.

AND ANGRY.

HI.

HELLO.

SO... UM, CAN I SIT HERE, TOO?

SURE. OF COURSE.

BUT TODAY IT'S SOMETHING MORE.

SORRY. I JUST REALLY HATE FATHER'S DAY.

ME, TOO.

DADDY ISSUES, *TOO*, HUH?

UH, *YEAH*.

I HEAR YOU.

YOURS IS... UH, *GONE*?

YUP. AS A DOORNAIL. YOURS?

PRISON.

OH. *GOTCHA*.

SO, *ANYWAY*...

...YOU LOOKED AWESOME AT MY PARTY.

I... *REALLY*?

YEAH, TOTALLY. THAT WHOLE ASIAN SCHOOLGIRL THING IS HOT. WHAT'S YOUR *ETHNICITY*?

MY, UH, *"ETHNICITY"*?

SORRY, TACKY QUESTION. MY FOUL.

NO. I JUST DON'T, UM... UNDERSTAND.

IT'S JUST YOU LOOK LIKE YOU MIGHT BE... *MIXED*.

MIXED?

MIXED *RACE*? Y'KNOW, LIKE YOUR DAD'S *WHITE* OR--

OH. YES. MY DAD'S *WHITE*.

SO, YOUR MOM'S... WHAT? CHINESE? KOREAN? THAI?

I... ...DON'T KNOW.

9

SOMETIMES IT'S RIGHT... THERE.

IN FRONT OF MY FACE.

WE HAVE THE SAME COLORING...

...AND I DON'T SEE IT.

AND THEN... SUDDENLY--

--IT'S ALL I CAN SEE.

IT'S TIME FOR ANSWERS.

YOU COULD HAVE CALLED.
I NEED TO... TALK.
ALL RIGHT.
UM... I WAS-- UH, WONDERING...
YES?
UM... DO YOU, UM, KNOW...
...UH, WHOM MY MOTHER IS?

I HAVE *IDEAS.*

NO, AND IT'S *"WHO."*

YOU... *PAUSED.*

ME, *TOO.*

I IMAGINE YOU *WOULD.*

ISN'T THERE A, UH, TEST? OR SOMETHING? I SAW ON TV--

THAT WOULD REQUIRE A BLOOD SAMPLE.

AND WE BOTH KNOW HOW DIFFICULT IT IS TO MAKE *HER* BLEED.

THERE WAS A TIME WHEN I SUSPECTED--

--DAMMIT.

YO, HOLD IT.

YOU TRYING TO TELL ME SOMETHING?

I MEAN, YOU WANNA TELL ME WHY I FEEL LIKE--

WHAT DO YOU MEAN?

--I'M FIGHTING SHIVA--

--AND NOT YOU?

DO YOU, UM, THINK THAT SHE COULD MAYBE--

--BE MY MOTHER?

WHAT MAKES YOU THINK I--

YOU *KNEW* HER.

NOT *THAT* LONG AGO. IT WAS--

"--JUST ABOUT TEN YEARS AGO SHE AND I WERE...

"...HANGING OUT.

"THE OLD LEAGUE OF ASSASSINS DAYS."

"DID YOU KNOW... CAIN, THEN?"

"KNEW WHO HE WAS."

"DID *SHE*?"

"WE *ALL* KNEW EACH OTHER.

"BUT THERE WAS THIS ONE TIME..."

NEVER ASKED HER ABOUT IT.

ME AND *SANDY* WEREN'T TIGHT LIKE *THAT.*

WAIT. SANDY?

OH! HA-HA! WELL, BEFORE SHE ANOINTED HERSELF *LADY SHIVA,* SHE WAS JUST PLAIN OL' *SANDRA WU-SAN* FROM DETROIT.

SANDRA? BUT *I'M*--

--CASSANDRA...

CAIN.
VISITOR.

WHO THE--

CASSANDRA?

WELL--
YOU NEED TO DO SOMETHING FOR ME.

YOU WANT ME--?

SURE. ANYTHING.

TELL ME--

--WHO MY MOTHER IS.

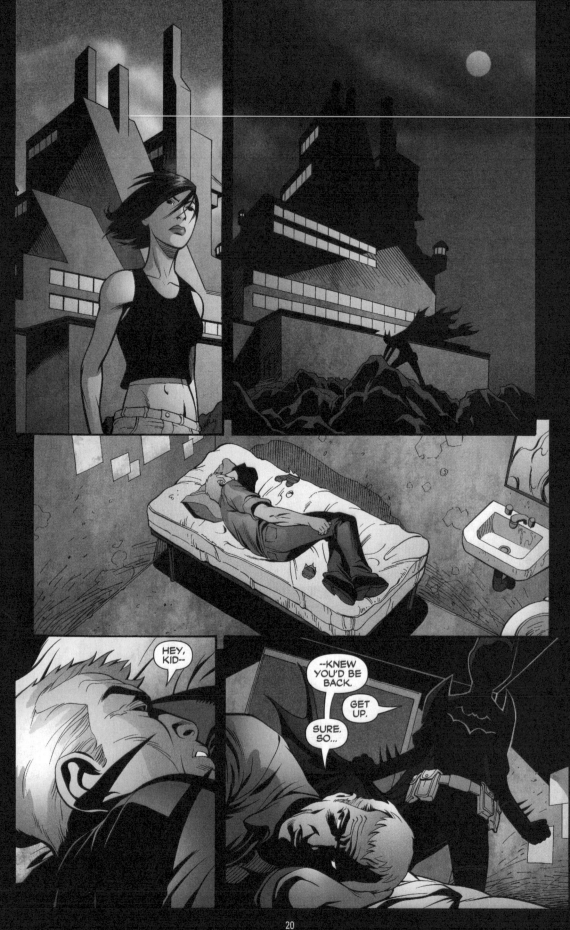

"Hitting Pavement"
Andy Kuhn – Art

FEELS SAD. PACKING AGAIN.

ON THE MOVE FOR SO LONG.

I HAVE A... PLACE, NOW. BUT--

--I NEED ANSWERS.

ABOUT MY MOTHER. WHOEVER SHE IS.

I HAVE A, UH, SUSPECT, THOUGH.

SHIVA ISN'T EASY TO FIND.

SO I'M BEGINNING AT HER, UM, BEGINNING.

I'M... HOMESICK ALREADY.

HEY, CASSANDRA.

WHAT'S UP? GOIN' SOME-WHERE?

UM... YEAH.

I WAS WONDERING, UM, WOULD YOU--

--TAKE CARE OF THIS?

IT'LL STAY RIGHT HERE 'TIL YOU GET BACK.

YEAH, SURE. TOTALLY.

THANKS, BRENDA.

UH, THANKS.

SO, UH...

UH-HUH?

...I'M ZERO.

CASSANDRA.

COOL NAME.

OH, UH, YEAH. UM, YOU, TOO.

SO, UMMM...

YEAH?

...I'VE GOT A LITTLE TIME.

DO YOU WANNA MAYBE...

"...GO FOR A RIDE?"

HE'S SCARED AT FIRST.

ME, TOO.

HIS HANDS...

...FEEL GOOD. IT'S WEIRD.

I DON'T EVEN KNOW HIM.

BUT I LIKE THIS.

HIM.

ME.

THE ROAD.

EVERYTHING.

I ALMOST FORGET--

I HAVE TO GO.

THAT'S COOL. BUT--

--ONE THING FIRST.

OKAY.

OKAY, SO... BYE.

I'LL SEE YOU.

WOW. SHE IS... THE COOLEST GIRL, EVER.

YOU KNOW HER?

A LITTLE, YEAH. WE BONDED OVER *PARENTAL* ISSUES.

MY SKIN FEELS... ALIVE.

WHERE HIS ARMS WERE. HIS LIPS.

I WONDER--

FOOD - GA
NEXT E

--DID CAIN AND SHIVA HAVE... FEELINGS?

IF I AM THEIRS...

...WAS IT PASSION?

LOVE?

OR WAS IT...

...WAS I... JUST, UH, BUSINESS?

AN EXPERIMENT.

OR AN ACCIDENT?

DOES IT MATTER?

ROUTE 66

IT'S A LONG RIDE TO DETROIT.

TOO LONG TO GO--

--WITHOUT EATING.

CHOMP 'N' CHUG
BAR AND GRILL

ENTRANCE

I'LL NEED MY STRENGTH.

THIS SOUNDS DUMB, BUT--

--SOMETIMES BEING A GIRL...

...FEELS AWFUL.

RESTROOMS

HEY, I'M GONNA NEED TO SEE SOME I.D.

I, UH, I JUST WANT A BURGER.

HMMM... ALL RIGHT. COMES WITH FRIES. THAT IT?

MAKE THAT TWO.

TWO BURGERS?

NO, THREE.

THREE--?

WITH CHEESE.

AND A BIG MILK.

PLEASE.

OKAY...

HEY, LENNY! ORDER UP!

WELL, WELL, AREN'T YOU A SIGHT FOR SORE THIGHS.

HEHHEH, GOOD ONE, TRAV.

YOU LOST, LITTLE GIRL?

EVEN WHEN I DON'T LOOK FOR IT...

...TROUBLE FINDS ME.

AW, NOW DON'T PRETEND YOU "NO SPEAK-Y ENGL-Y."

Y'KNOW, I ALWAYS WANTED TO MAKE IT WITH A CHINESE CHICK.

THEN GO TO CHINA.

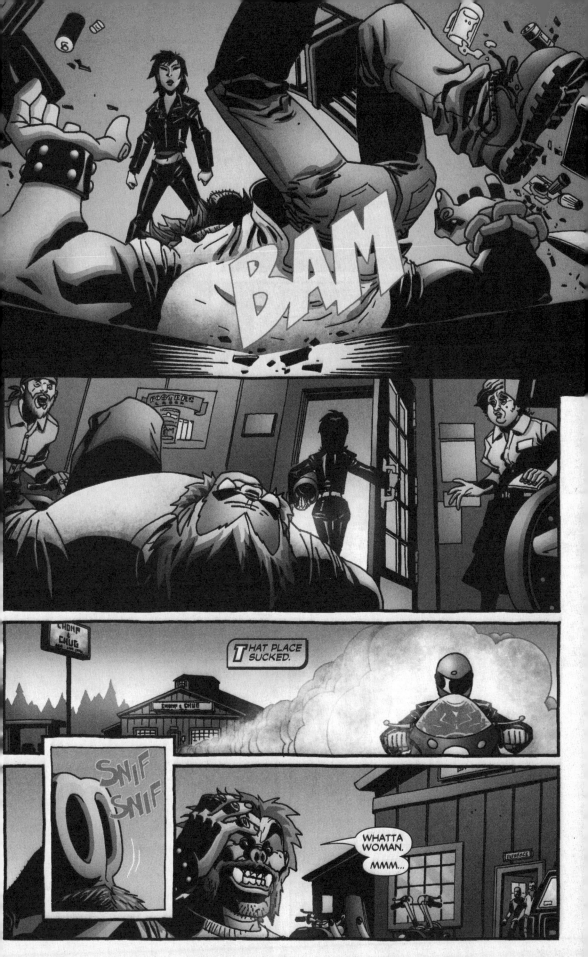

I SMELL IT FIRST.
HER CHILDHOOD.
WHEN I SEE IT...
...IT HITS ME.
WHAT IF? IF SHE IS...
...AM I DIFFERENT FOR, UM... KNOWING?
WE'LL SEE.
REMINDS ME OF FT. JOE'S. OF HOME.
DOES THAT MEAN... SOMETHING?
TILLBROOK
THEATER
WORK FOR
HER ONLY ADDRESS.
OKAY... NOW, WHAT?
HM.

HERE. LEMME HELP.

WELL, AREN'T YOU A NICE GIRL.

YOU LIVED HERE... LONG?

OH, MY, YES, FORTY YEARS.

UM, I WAS HOPING, YOU MIGHT, UH, LOOK AT THIS--

BATMAN HAD IT. IT'S SHIVA. SANDRA, THEN.

AND HER SISTER, CAROLYN, AFTER HER, UH, MURDER--

--SANDRA LEAVES. BECOMES... SHIVA.

WHAT? WHAT'S THE--

HEYA, SPUNKY, MISS ME?

THAT. WAS. NOT...

...COOL!

I MISJUDGE HIM. AGAIN.

AND SHE'LL PAY THE PRICE.

NO!

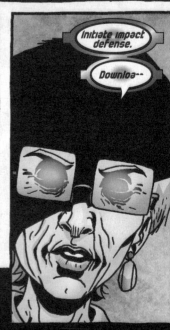

Initiate impact defense.

Downloa--

KEERASH

NO.

WHAT DID I DO?

"Bird Calls"
Alé Garza – Pencils  Jesse Delperdang – Inks

"RA'S AL GHUL CREATED THE LEAGUE OF ASSASSINS TO BE 'THE FANG THAT PROTECTS HIS HEAD.'

"BUT HE WASN'T SATISFIED WITH THE FICKLE LOYALTIES OF MOST MERCENARIES.

"WHEN HE LEARNED OF CAIN'S *THEORIES*, RA'S PROVIDED HIM WITH...SUBJECTS, HOPING TO CREATE HIS NEXT GENERATION OF ASSASSINS.

"IT WAS A CATASTROPHE. THE FEW THAT SURVIVED INFANCY TURNED ON EACH OTHER--

"--UNTIL ONLY ONE REMAINED.

"CAIN HAD AN *UBU* PUT HIM DOWN LIKE A MAD DOG.

"BUT IT GAVE CAIN AN IDEA. INSTEAD OF ONE MAN TRAINING A NEW LEAGUE, THE LEAGUE WOULD TRAIN ONE CHILD.

"AFTER THE FIRST FEW DIED, HE DETERMINED THAT GENETICS WAS THE KEY.

"SO, CAIN HAD YOU. RA'S CALLED *YOU*...

"...THE ONE WHO IS ALL."

ONLY THE ENTIRE LEAGUE COULD'VE TAKEN DOWN SHIVA.

SHE... UM, WASN'T SHE "IN ON IT," *TOO*?

SHIVA WANTED TO "SAVE YOU FOR LATER."

YOU GOTTA UNDERSTAND, THIS WAS A LONG TIME AGO. SHE WASN'T MUCH OLDER THAN YOU ARE NOW. SHE WASN'T *UNBEATABLE* YET.

YOU UNDERSTAND WHAT I'M SAYING?

AND BEFORE YOU ASK...

...ONLY SHE AND CAIN KNOW THE ANSWER FOR SURE.

AND MY GUESS IS YOUR OLD MAN WON'T TELL YOU SQUAT.

I... UM...

YOU KNOW WHERE SHIVA IS?

NOPE. RAN AFOUL OF HER A FEW MONTHS BACK.

BUT I'M PRETTY MUCH OUTTA THE SCENE, NOW. MY TIME WITH THE DRAGON MADE ME DECIDE TO PUT STAKES IN THIS PLACE. GIVE SOME LOST KIDS A DIRECTION.

TEACH THEM TO FIGHT THE GOOD FIGHT, THIS TIME. CREATE MY OWN LEGACY.

WELL, THANK YOU--

NO. I DON'T DESERVE TO SHAKE YOUR HAND.

I JUST CHANGED MY STRIPES, IS ALL. BUT YOU--

--HUMBLE ME.

WE MADE YOU A WARRIOR.

YOU MADE YOURSELF A HERO.

YOU'RE... SICK?

GETTING BETTER.

GOOD.

SO ABOUT WHAT HAPPENED--

NOT HERE FOR THAT.

OKAY... SO WHAT DO YOU NEED?

I NEED TO FIND SHIVA.

SHIVA? WHY WOULD YOU--

I...THINK SHE'S MY MOTHER.

OKAY.

WHAP

SLAP

WHUD

IS
THIS A...
JOKE?

WHAT THE HELL?

I COULDN'T *BREATHE,* CASSANDRA.

JEEZ. A LITTLE EXTREME, DON'T YOU THINK?

CAN'T BREATHE, CAN'T *SCREAM.*

I... THAT WAS WRONG. BUT I SAW...DECEIT AND--

--HOW'D YOU LEARN--?

CAN YOU KEEP A SECRET?

SHIVA WANTS ME TO BE HER APPRENTICE.

WHAT?

SHE SENDS ME THESE LETTERS. THAT'S HOW I LEARNED THOSE MOVES.

YOU'RE THE ONLY PERSON I'VE TOLD.

YOU DIDN'T KNOW...I'M LOOKING FOR HER?

SO, *THAT'S* WHY YOU FREAKED.

SHIVA WANTS TO... *TEACH?*

LUCKILY, AND PLEASE DON'T TELL DINAH, I'VE BEEN TRYING TO KEEP AN EYE ON SHIVA AS BEST ONE CAN.

THIS IS THIRTY-EIGHT HOURS AGO IN A MONTENEGRO TRAIN STATION.

SHE COULD BE *ANYWHERE* BY NOW.

I DON'T THINK SO, BECAUSE WITHIN TWELVE HOURS--

GOOD EYE. THE OTHERS ARE KNOWN MERCS, TOO.

NOW, THIS IS WHERE THE CONJECTURE BEGINS...

THAT'S SHRIKE.

THIS IS NYSSA RAATKO, THE FIRST-BORN DAUGHTER OF RA'S AL GHUL. SHE MURDERED HIM AND INHERITED HIS EMPIRE.

ALL MY BEST INTEL POINTS TO HER HEADQUARTERS BEING LOCATED SOMEWHERE IN THE NEARBY BALKAN MOUNTAINS.

I'M NOT SURE OF HER CONNECTION WITH SHIVA...

THE LEAGUE OF ASSASSINS.

HM. COULD BE. NYSSA'S BEEN PRETTY QUIET SO FAR IN ESTABLISHING HERSELF IN HER FATHER'S SHOES.

REVITALIZING THE LEAGUE WOULD BE ON HER AGENDA.

BUT SHIVA WOULD NEVER GO BACK TO--

NO.

SHE'S THE NEW... SENSEI.

MY GOD. OF COURSE.

CASSANDRA, THAT WAS REALLY SMART THI--

DON'T PATTERNIZE ME.

I'M NOT--

--AND, IT'S "PAT-RO--"

HMM. NEVER MIND.

ZINDA. HOW FAST CAN YOU GET US TO THE BALKANS?

THREE HOURS TOPS, SKIPPER.

MAKE IT SOONER. IF YOU CAN.

I GOT VISUAL, CHIEF.

...THE ONLY ROAD FOR MILES. DON'T EVEN KNOW IF IT LEADS TO THE AL GHUL STRONGHOLD.

HOW? BIG *GUNS*?

THAT'S SOMETHING YOU'LL HAVE TO DISCOVER FOR YOURSELF, AND THE BEST WAY TO KEEP YOUR INVESTIGATION UNINTERRUPTED IS--

KEEP A HOLDING POSITION, ZINDA.

SORRY, WE'LL GET BACK TO *READING*. RIGHT NOW, IT'S TIME FOR A PLAN.

--TO TAKE OUT THAT ROAD.

NOPE. BIG *LUNGS*.

OH, MAN.

AND SINCE WE CAN'T LAND...

IT'S A GOOD THING I LIKE YOU, KID.

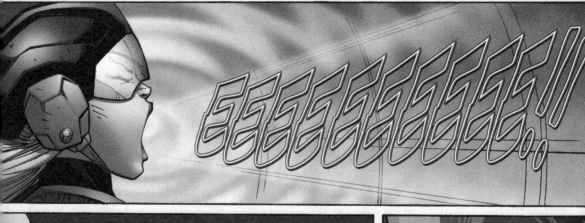

GOOD WORK, DINAH.

AW, SHUCKS. IT WEREN'T NOTHIN'.

BEFORE YOU GO...

THANKS FOR CALLING. DON'T WAIT SO LONG NEXT TIME, OKAY?

OKAY. BUT--

BUT, WHAT?

THE PHONE'S TWO-WAYS.

TOUCHÉ.

I HOPE YOU FIND WHAT YOU'RE LOOKING FOR.

GOOD LUCK.

YOU, TOO.

**"Motherlode"**
Pop Mhan – Pencils  Alé Garza – Pencils/Layouts  Jesse Delperdang – Inks/Finishes

NO, SENSEI.

GOOD. MOVING FORWARD...

THE UBU. BORN TO SERVE RA'S AL GHUL.

NOT MANY LEFT.

AND NYSSA USES THE WOMEN.

EXTRA, UH... PROTECTION. FROM WHO?

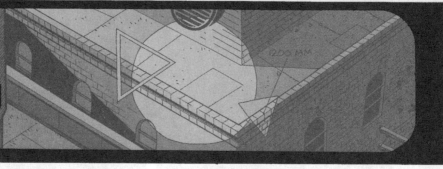

12.00 MM

PLUS A NEW LEAGUE.

NYSSA'S GOT PLANS.

BIG ONES.

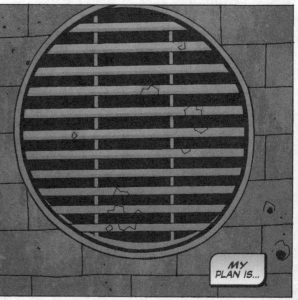

MY PLAN IS...

...TO NOT TURN BACK.

WAP

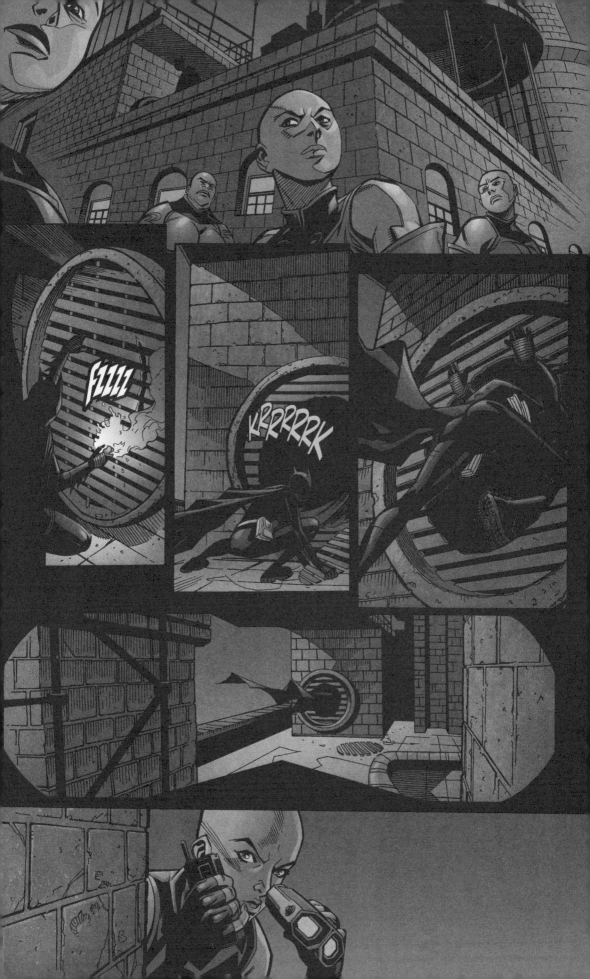

TIME'S SHORT.

DON'T EVEN HAVE A PLAN. SO STUPID...

WHAT AM I DOING?

SHE'S ALMOST THERE,

AND DOESN'T EVEN KNOW IT.

LET'S GIVE HER SOME DIRECTION, SHALL WE?

TK

SHUNK

THE SUSPENSE IS KILLING ME.

WALLS WON'T CUT.

FZZZ

WHY? DOES IT FEEL TOO *GOOD*?

THE WORSHIP?

CAIN? HOW DOES--

NOT *THAT* FATHER.

THE ONE YOU TRY SO DESPERATELY TO EMULATE.

YOUR *DADDY* KNOWS ALL ABOUT THAT.

BUT THAT'S NOT WHO YOU ARE.

NOT WHO YOU ARE *MEANT* TO--

JUST STOP THEM.

:CLAP:
:CLAP:

ALLOW ME TO INTRODUCE YOU TO YOUR STUDENTS.

MY--??

DON'T BE RUDE. ALL QUESTIONS IN DUE TIME.

NO. I CAN SEE. PERFECTLY.

YOU'RE SCARED.

SCARED? OF WHAT?

AND THINGS GET MORE INTRIGUING. TOO BAD.

CAN'T AFFORD TO LOSE EITHER ONE.

YOU'RE SCARED TO--

SORRY TO INTERRUPT--

KLK

--YOUR WORK.

BUT I NEED YOUR SERVICES.

NOW.

--ANSWER ME!!!

ENOUGH GAMES!

OR BOTH?

TELL ME--

HURNN?!

SHHRACK

**"Love's Labors..."**
Pop Mhan – Pencils  Jesse Delperdang & Robin Riggs – Inks

BATMAN WOULD BE MAD.

DIDN'T THINK.

ACTED ON FEELING.

NOW I'M STUCK. TRAPPED.

I HATE THAT. A LOT.

DIDN'T PLAN ON MR. FREEZE.

CAME TO FIND OUT IF SHIVA'S MY MOM.

FOUND SHE'S... TEACHING THE LEAGUE OF ASSASSINS.

FOR NYSSA. HER DAD, RA'S AL GHUL, HE, UH, PAID FOR MY DAD'S...EXPERIMENT.

ME.

THIS ISN'T YOUR CONCERN, NYSSA.

MY DEAR SHIVA, I BEG TO DIFFER.

GIVEN MY FATHER'S INVESTMENT IN THIS MARVEL OF HUMAN ENGINEERING--

--I HAVE EVERY CLAIM TO HER. THAT IS, OF COURSE--

--UNLESS YOU HAVE A PERSONAL OBJECTION.

I'M SURE YOU KNOW ABOUT THE LEGENDARY RESTORATIVE PROPERTIES OF THE *LAZARUS PIT.*

BUT DID YOU KNOW THAT MINE IS *REUSABLE?*

JUST A SMALL EXAMPLE OF HOW I'M IMPROVING ON MY FATHER'S LEGACY.

I OFFER A *CHOICE.* DIE A COLD, MEANINGLESS DEATH, OR--

--TAKE YOUR BIRTHRIGHT AT MY SIDE AND HELP SAVE HUMANITY FROM ITSELF.

BEEP

*TALIA.* RIGHT ON TIME.

MY BELOVED SISTER, WHAT'S THE NEWS?

ARE THE *OTHERS* WITH YOU?

*NYSSA,* THIS BETTER NOT BE A DELAY ON *FREEZE'S*--

AT YOUR REQUEST,

ON THE CONTRARY, WE WILL BE OPERATIONAL BY TOMORROW. BY NEXT WEEK, HALF THE WORLD'S OIL RESERVES WILL BE *FROZEN.* SOLID.

--VAST STOCKPILES OF FOOD ROT, WHILE PEOPLE STARVE.

MILLIONS DIE FROM TREATABLE DISEASES, WHILE DRUG COMPANIES RAKE IN BILLIONS.

THE ENVIRONMENT CHOKES ON OUR WASTE, BECOMING SO TOXIC THAT LIFE FAILS.

IT'S *GENOCIDE* BY GREED, APATHY AND NEGLECT.

THESE ARE THE *REAL* CRIMES.

SOMETHING MUST CHANGE.

BUT THEY'RE... *EVIL.*

THE *SOCIETY'S* PLANS ARE VAST, BATGIRL. THEY WILL SUCCEED. I CAN'T STOP THEM.

WHEN THE WORLD GETS A TRUE TASTE OF VIOLENT OPPRESSION AND THEIR HEROES LIE DEAD AND BROKEN--

--APATHY WILL DIE.

THAT'S WHEN YOU'LL LEAD MY LEAGUE TO SANCTION KEY SOCIETY MEMBERS.

LEAVING TALIA AND I TO LEAD THE REVOLUTION. A NEW WORLD WILL BE BORN. ONE OF PEACE AND EQUALITY. MILLIONS OF LIVES WILL BE SAVED.

YOU'LL BE A HERO.

HEROES DON'T KILL.

NEED TO STOP... ALL OF THIS.

NYSSA IS... CRUEL.

LIFE IS CRUEL.

NOT ALWAYS.

YES. ALWAYS. I FINALLY FELT LIKE I COULD MOVE ON--

--AND THAT WITCH DANGLES HOPE LIKE A CARROT TO MAKE ME CREATE THESE MACHINES.

IF I HELP HER, SHE SAYS SHE CAN SAVE MY NORA.

BUT NORA'S... GONE. THE PIT CAN'T--

HER BRAIN'S INTACT.

SHE MIGHT STILL BE...

...IN THERE.

NYSSA SAYS SHE NEEDS TO ADJUST THE ALCHEMY OF THE PIT TO BEST SERVE NORA'S "UNIQUE CIRCUMSTANCE."

SHE'S PLAYING YOU.

NO!

SPLOOOSH

IT'S...IT'S FINALLY OVER.

WAIT. LOOK--

BATGIRL #70  Art by Tim Sale

"The Resurrection and the Life"
Pop Mhan – Pencils  Jesse Delperdang & Dan Davis – Inks

I WAS TRAPPED.

UH-OH.

NEEDED OUT.

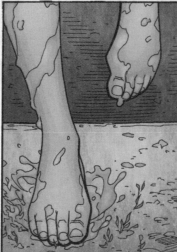

TO STOP NYSSA.

NO!

I MADE A CHOICE.

A DEAL. WITH FREEZE. HE FREED ME.

NORA!

I HELPED FREE HIS WIFE. TO FREE HIM.

I MESSED UP.

AGAIN.

SHE WHO IS *RISEN*—

—TO BRING DEATH TO LIFE.

*SRSHKKH*

OH... ...$#%!

AND LIFE TO DEATH.

BECAUSE OF ME—

LOOK AT ME! YOU MADE ME THIS UNNATURAL THING!

—PEOPLE DIE.

*GAKK!*

My HEART ONLY KNOWS ONE THING...

...KILLING IS WRONG.

NO MATTER WHAT. OR WHO.

NO! YOU FOOL!

ISN'T IT?

SHE HAS NO EFFECT ON ME! ONLY I CAN--

I WON'T LET YOU KILL--

HAVE YOU LEARNED NOTHING?!? SHE MUST BE STOPPED BEFORE--

TOO LATE, DEMON-SPAWN.

I FOUND THEM.

AND NOW THEY FIND YOU.

RISE!

WHAT THE--?? HOW IS SHE DOING--

SHE WAS TOO BROKEN AND ALTERED BY YEARS OF YOUR...MACHINES, SHE'S ABSORBED THE PIT'S ALCHEMY! WARPED IT TO RAISE THE DEAD!

$#&%! THERE'S *HUNDREDS*--

I BUILT ON THE SITE OF ONE OF MILOSEVIC'S "ETHNIC CLEANSINGS" TO REMIND ME OF *TRUE EVIL.* TO--

SHUT IT.

JUST TELL ME--

--ARE THEY... *ALIVE?*

NO.

WATCH FREEZE CHASE HIS... LOVE AWAY.

NYSSA'S PLANS ARE RUINED. THE SOCIETY'S, TOO.

EVERYTHING. AND I...UH...

...NEVER GOT MY ANSWER.

ABOUT SHIVA.

BUT MAYBE I GOT ONE--

--ABOUT ME.

ONE-WHO-IS-ALL?

WHAT... WHAT DO WE DO NOW?

**"Prey for Her"**
Pop Mhan – Pencils  Jesse Delperdang – Inks

**Once upon a time...**

...there was a man named Câin.

He had a very special kind of job.

Câin was a PEOPLE HUNTER.

One of the best in all the land, but the very nature of his work--

--made Câin a lonely man.

And lonely men get IDEAS.

About what to leave BEHIND.

So, the lonely hunter made a wish ...

NATURAL THINGS.

THINGS DIE--

--AND GIRLS CHANGE.

IN THE WOODS.

I LEFT BEHIND DEATH.

DESTRUCTION.

ALL 'CAUSE I WANTED TO KNOW--

--ABOUT MY MOM. MY PAST. MY STORY.

SO... SELFISH.

SOME HERO.

SOMETIMES STORIES ARE... WRONG, TOO.

SOMETIMES WISHES DON'T COME TRUE.

JUST WANTED TO GO HOME. TO BLÜDHAVEN.

FIRST PLACE THAT'S EVER BEEN...MINE.

AND SEE BRENDA. MY FRIEND. SHE'S... KIND. TRULY.

AND ZERO. I MISS WATCHING HIM...WATCH ME. WANT ME.

I MISS TEA.

ROAD WAS OUT.

FASTER TO HIKE.

OX, TIGRIS AND WHITE WILLOW FOLLOWED ME.

FROM THE LEAGUE OF ASSASSINS.

I SAVED THEM. THEY KIND OF... WORSHIP ME.

THEY CALL ME--

--ONE-WHO-IS-ALL?

JUST *BATGIRL*.

*BATGIRL*. FORGIVE MY BOLDNESS, WHAT DID YOU DO TO DEFEAT THE LADY SHIVA?

YEAH, LOVE TO KNOW THAT MYSELF.

OH, *um*, I...WELL, IT WAS LIKE, *uhh*...

...AND I, UH...

AHEM.

I SAW HOW SHE'S *LIKE* ME.

*WEAK* WHERE I AM.

HUNGRY TO KNOW SHE'S... *HUMAN*.

SHE'S HUNGRY TO--

--STOP.

WHAT'S THE--

*shh.*

THAT IS...

WHAT THIS IS...ALL ABOUT.

ISN'T IT?

IMPRESSING *HER.*

YOU'RE NOT EVEN IMPRESSING *ME.*

YOU'RE ALL TOO... LIMITED. BY YOUR "STYLES."

HE TAUGHT ME... TEAMWORK.

BUT IT'S NOT A TEAM. MORE HIS *FAMILY.*

WISH IT STILL FELT LIKE THAT.

I HAD A REAL TEAM, ONCE.

I WASN'T "BATGIRL."

WE SAVED THE WORLD.*

*EDITOR'S NOTE: SEE JUSTICE LEAGUE ELITE.

NOW, I LEAD. AND IT WORKS.

THEY START TO... SAVE THEMSELVES.

THEY ALWAYS DO.

BATGIRL #72  Art by Tim Sale

"Turning Abel"
Francisco Rodriguez de la Fuente – Pencils  Jesse Delperdang & Rodney Ramos – Inks

And so the guard set the boy free...

...and into the wild.

The hunter and the demon never learned of what the guard did.

Of what the boy became.

But the demon's daughter did. And she gave the boy (now a man) his birthright. His home. His family.

She taught him who he was. Who he was supposed to be.

And of the girl who took his place...

DAMMIT, I COULD'VE--

NO MORE KILLING!!!

EXACTLY!! HOW MANY MORE WILL *HE* KILL??

YOU CAN'T *FIX* HIM, DO YOU *UNDERSTAND?* HE CAN'T CHANGE. HE'S NOT LIKE ME! OR YOU!

KILLING IS *KILLING.*

"AND KILLING'S *WRONG.*"

STAY WITH TIGRIS.

WE DO THIS MY WAY.

AND NO ONE DIES.

YEAH, 'CAUSE THAT'S BEEN WORKIN' REAL WELL SO FAR...

YOU NOT BAT!

BATS FLY!

YOU JUSS JUMMP!

183

IS THAT A "YES"?

WE SHOULD GO AND--

NO. YOU'RE STAYING RIGHT HERE. I'M SURE BATGIRL IS--

--DID YOU HEAR THAT?

I...MY EARS ARE STILL RINGING.

PROBABLY A SQUIRREL, BUT ON THE SAFE SIDE...

Glurg!

BATGIRL!

FWUMP

FOR ME? WHY DID SHE DO THIS FOR ME? I'M NOT WORTHY--

BECAUSE EVERYONE'S WORTHY OF THE CHANCE TO CHANGE.

Yesss... you fnnly unnerstan... me.

I win.

NOT LIKE THIS.

I REFUSE.

NO.

PUT HER DOWN. I KNOW WHAT YOU'RE THINKING. AND I WON'T LET YOU.

LET ME?

KRAK

AND SHE DIED SAVING *YOU.* TO GIVE YOU A CHOICE.

BUT TRY STOPPING ME AGAIN. I WILL TAKE THAT CHOICE AWAY.

*SHE* IS THE HERO.

I AM NOT.

NEVER HAVE BEEN.

**A long time ago...**

... the lonely hunter's dreams kept dying.

And he realized the problem.

The children were not HIS children.

Not of his flesh. His blood. His strength.

He realized that to have the perfect child...

...he needed the perfect woman... to be the perfect mother.

And so, the lonely hunter searched the world looking for her.

And one day, in the far-off kingdom of Detroit, Michigan, Cain found his perfect bride.

And he killed her.

"Revelations"
Pop Mhan – Pencils   Jesse Delperdang & Adam DeKraker – Inks

Long ago and so far away...

...in the land of Detroit, lived two sisters. Though as different as night and day, they loved each other deeply. And more than that--

--they loved to dance. Every moment of the day was spent in lessons.

They danced all through the night. They danced so much it became the secret language of sisters.

People like the lonely hunter, Cain.

The world had never seen anything quite like it. People would come from near and far to watch the sisters perform.

And Cáin watched the dancing sisters. He watched how the sisters balanced each other.

He watched the younger sister allow her older sister to hold her back and keep her down.

Out of love.

He saw in the younger sister the sparks of the same fire that burned in his own heart.

He just had to fan the flames.

Give the young dancer reason to burn.

ARRRGH!

THWIP

UNGH!!

THWUMP

STOP!
YOUR MIND IS CLOUDED.

YOU CAN FEEL IT.

THE RAGE OF REBIRTH.

WE PROCEED WITH CLEAR MINDS, ONLY.

YES?!?

TAKE CONTROL.

OF YOUR BREATH. YOUR BLOOD.

OF THE BODY I GAVE YOU.

THAT'S IT.

THAT'S RIGHT.

TO KILL.

HIM.

AT FIRST, IT WAS PETTY, SIMPLE REVENGE.

I WASN'T PREPARED FOR WHAT I'D FIND.

WHEN I FOUND HIM, JUST LIKE HE WANTED, WITH THE LEAGUE OF ASSASSINS...

...I DIDN'T KNOW HOW MUCH MY SISTER HAD KEPT ME BACK.

UNTIL THEY SHOWED ME EVERYTHING I WAS CAPABLE OF.

WITHOUT HER.

YOUR FATHER FREED ME FROM HER.

HE GAVE ME MY LIFE. MY PURPOSE.

I WAS GRATEFUL.
HE SPARED MY LIFE...
...WITH A PROPOSITION.
AND I ACCEPTED.
THE CHANCE TO BECOME SOMEONE NEW.
NO. NOT SOME*ONE.*
I WANTED TO BECOME...
...SOME*THING.*

JUST TELL ME...HOW MANY?

KILLED.

SINCE WE FOUGHT.

WILL YOU EVER STOP?

WITH MY OWN HANDS?

FORTY-EIGHT.

IT'S WHY I HAD YOU.

I'M READY.

Once upon a time...
...there was a girl.
Born to be something unlike the world had ever seen.
A dancing hunter.
But she didn't want that. And so, she ran away.
Hungry and desperate, she found salvation in the dark flap of wings.
She thought she was a bat. But she came to find she wasn't that either.
She was only a runaway girl...
...named Cain.
THE END